Young
PILLARS

By
Charles M. Schulz

**The Creator
of "Peanuts"
Takes a Look
at Church
Young People**

THE WARNER PRESS
ANDERSON, INDIANA

About this book and its author . . .

Charles M. Schulz is widely known as the award-winning creator of Charlie Brown, Linus, Lucy, Snoopy, and other little people who inhabit the popular "Peanuts" cartoon strip. His quiet wit and keen powers of observation into human nature have won him millions of daily readers.

An active Christian layman, Mr. Schulz in this book turns his attention to church young people. The editors believe you will be entertained by these pages. At the same time, as Mr. Schulz has pointed out, no artist goes before the public without communicating some kind of message. We believe these cartoons speak both to youth and to older readers on behalf of a well-rounded Christian philosophy of life. Many of these cartoons have been published widely in church youth periodicals where their enthusiastic reception has led to the preparation of this book.

Mr. Schulz has prepared these cartoons with a sense of stewardship and as a contribution to the life of the church. Warner Press is indebted to Mr. Schulz, to United Feature Syndicate, and to Rinehart & Company, whose co-operation has made this publication possible.

—The Editors

"Today we're supposed to start a study of the journeys of the Apostle Paul."

"I appreciate being nominated as president of our youth group, but I am afraid that I must decline on the grounds that I am too stupid!"

"I thought she was saving my letters because she liked me. . . . Now, I find out it's because the church is having a paper drive."

"I've been honking for twenty minutes, but I guess the motor drowns out the horn."

"I think I like pledging better than tithing. . . . It doesn't involve so much arithmetic!"

"Oh, yeah? Well, I'll bet I'm **twice** as humble as you are!"

"I don't think you have held my hand once since
you became treasurer of the youth group!"

"I think we're quite lucky to have been born into the first society in all history that is dominated by teen-agers!"

"What do you mean, I don't look feminine?
I have a ribbon in my hair, haven't I?"

"I don't know. . . . I think if I were a minister, I wouldn't even want me in the congregation."

"What I'd like to be is a perfectionist . . . but I don't know
how to do anything!"

"The insane suggestion that we purchase seven-hundred dollar Hi-Fi sets for each of the Sunday school rooms has been turned down. Is there any more old business?"

"Either we're going to have a special number on the musical saw, or I'm sitting next to a member of the Building Committee."

"Can't we go somewhere, and sit down?"

"That was our pastor. . . . He said if he had to eat one
more 'hot dish,' he'd die!"

"Haven't you heard? Right after the evening service there's going to be a wiener roast!"

"Maybe the girls didn't hear the doorbell the first time.
. . . I'll ring it again."

"Beat by a girl! It never would have happened, but I hit one of my brilliant streaks of mediocrity!"

"As I stand here looking at the universe, some-how being recently appointed program chairman for the annual picnic no longer seems frighten-ing!"

"He gave me his sweater!"

"I regret to report that our proposal to play Perry Como records at the next missionary meeting has been met with stern opposition."

"I'm writing home to tell my mother about how the boy's camp is separated from our camp by a raging stream!"

"Strange thing with Alfred. . . . First we involved him in Youth Fellowship, then we involved him in Men's Brotherhood, then we involved him in Sunday School visitation. . . . Finally we involved him right out of the church!"

"Wally Nelson will now lead us in a discussion entitled, 'It Doesn't Matter What You Believe, Just So You Believe Something.'"

"Stop singing, 'Wash Me, and I Shall be Whiter Than Snow'!"

"I've been won over to envelope-giving."

"He wants me to wear his school letter, but . . . well . . .
I don't know."

"Brother Forbes' preaching on Sodom and Go-morrah never fails to thrill me!"

"Somebody put in a charge-a-plate!"

"I think maybe I got on too many rivets. . . . I can't move!"

"I may not work very fast, but I sure do a sloppy job!"

"This is my new boyfriend. . . . I call him 'Stewardship' because it took a lot of planning to catch him!"

"Okay! All set for the wieners!"

"These are perfect attendance pins . . . Sunday School, Youth Fellowship, Youth Leader Training, Men's Brotherhood, Youth Work Night, Men's Work Night, Youth Missions, Youth Recreation, Vacation School, Bible Camp, Youth Bible Camp, City Youth Camp, County Youth Camp, State Youth Camp, International Youth Camp, and Choir Practice. . . . I haven't been home in three months!"

"Would our church's future missionary to New Guinea kindly tell me what he was doing down at the drugstore with Elaine Ramsperger instead of me?"

"All right, so they're all wrong doctrinally. . . . You can sit on their bench anyway, can't you?"

"Of course, my idea of a real success would be to own a big place with my own swimming pool, my own tennis court, and my own drag-strip!"

"Don't knock yourself out, Ma. . . . I get the hint!"

"I just remembered something. . . . I don't know how to sing!"

"I thought maybe we could sing choruses."

"It's my big brother's sweat-shirt. . . . I thought for sure it would fit me if I rolled up the sleeves!"

"I knocked 'em all over. . . . How come I can't keep them?"

"I don't have dates on Saturday nights because I feel I should study my Sunday school lesson. . . . Besides, nobody ever asks me!"

"Didn't anybody bring food?!"

"He asked me if I'd accept a nomination to be Program Chairman of the youth group this coming year, and when I said, 'Yes,' he fainted!"

"What worries me is that if I decide to go into the ministry, and if I get married, and if I have some children, will those children want to be the children of a minister?"

"So you paid for the hamburgers and everything. . . . Don't look at it as not being your duty. . . . Look at it as being good stewardship!"

"I wish you wouldn't always refer to our dates as 'fel-lowship'!"

"I'm very happy to be a part of a confused generation, because I never have been able to figure out whether I'm coming or going!"

"I would have liked to have owned it when it was new, but of course when it was new, I wasn't even born yet!"

"I think the presence of my car does a lot for our church.
. . . It proves we're a struggling young congregation!"

"That's a special songbook I designed. . . . The pages are
blank so all the little kids can have something to write
in during the morning service!"

"I was telling my dad how they say it isn't the kids that are delinquent, it's their parents. So he says then it could be it's not the parents either—it's the grandparents!"

"I really have nothing against your saving string, Son, but couldn't you at least keep it rolled in a ball?"

"I do too like to walk in the rain. . . . I just like to see who I'm walking with, that's all!"

"Only four of us showed up for choir practice, Dad, but that didn't discourage us. . . . It just made the four of us feel real faithful."

"If you really liked me, you'd come and watch me play softball, but I'm glad you're not because I don't want you to see what a terrible player I am!"

"I always put some initials at the bottom of my letters to make people think I have a secretary."

"During the Christmas program I couldn't remember any of my lines, and now I can't forget 'em!"

"I think she's the most beautiful girl I've seen in my whole life . . . or rather, this year . . . this month . . . this week . . . well, maybe during the last twenty minutes."

"See that new church? I helped fix the flat tire on the truck that hauled the papers for the paper sale that paid for the wood that they used to build the front steps!"

"I received this set of Bible commentaries for my birth-day. They're so beautiful I'm almost tempted to go into the ministry!"

"We disagree theologically. . . . He thinks he's perfect, and I think he isn't!"